New Passengers

New Passengers
by Tine Høeg

Translated from the Danish
by Misha Hoekstra

Lolli Editions

you can't write me
I'll write you

August

*

I've bought a monthly pass

I've been assigned a new name

a teacher's name

comprised of four letters
from my first and last names

I've been given the code to the high school network
which is changed every six months according to the principle

summer16 winter16 summer17 winter17

I've been briefed
on the systems

it's by chance
we fall to talking on the train
my first day of teaching

I'm nervous and our legs
graze each other
when we sit down

you're a graphic designer at a travel agency

you're a commuter too

you're ten years older than me

you're married and father to a girl

*

I look at my reflection in a store window
at Copenhagen Central Station on Tuesday

I buy two cups of coffee
and position myself on the escalator

turns out
you've done the same thing

we board with the cups

I donate mine to two teenagers
who sit leaning up against each other
looking tired

they're happy and surprised

blood in my body

a thrumming in my ears
when the train starts to move

*

the first time I see you naked:

train toilet

someplace between Copenhagen and Næstved

I've never wanted

someone this way before

*

feels as if I've got a fever

the students resemble each other

have the same names

skinny legs big sneakers

four classes of Danish
one as homeroom teacher

homeroom teacher

the classrooms are hot

a smell of sweat
perfume

pasta and tuna
from the boys' plastic tubs

they eat during class

I can't recognize my voice
when I stand at my desk and talk

the students' eyes

I scratch at my cheek

each group must bring a set of camping cookware

my colleague STAR has interrupted my teaching
to talk about the intro trip

he teaches Danish and history
and walks around in a T-shirt with the legend:

moral beacon

his beard thick and well trimmed

I wonder if he's ever felt the way
I feel now

it *is* tough at the start says EMO

she teaches drama and painting

but after three four years it becomes more manageable

hundreds of peacock eyes
stare at me from her skirt

hi Mom
written in marker

winter is coming
written in ballpoint

I'm out on the toilet
every lunch hour with my coffee

I gaze at the graffiti

hearts stars

an alien

where do you go during lunch?

EMO passes me in the coatroom on Friday
and drags me to the cafeteria

high ceiling and hubbub

the teachers sitting together

special of the day on plastic trays

STAR talks loudly and shovels it in

something Asian

also a salad bar for tossing something together

five kinds of dressing in tubes

you grab me a napkin?

I tell you the last period yesterday

are the tomatoes from your greenhouse?

BROM pours crab salad onto a slice of black rye

her husband owns a fish restaurant

LUST teaches math and physics

she taps an egg against the table

EMO asks are they your own?

I say nothing

I glance at the their mouths
and out the window:

the parking lot and the vast Bilka

STAR says something funny and everyone laughs

I sit with the stem from a pear

you twist the top off a cola

you unpack a sandwich
from some tinfoil
some three miles from here

my pulse quickens with the thought

your hands around the bread

a small trail of spit from your mouth
when you take a bite

*

the second time I see you naked:

between bushes in a park

we got out in Ringsted

I'm off early

you told them at the agency
that you had a meeting

your body is softer
than the bodies I'm used to but

your cock's incredibly hard

you draw my finger
down across your face
and take it into your mouth

August begins to glow

you've got broad hands

dirty nails

you open your eyes wide when we kiss

as if you're surprised to see me

you have a tattoo
on the inside of your upper arm

a small wreath with a name inside

what's it say? I ask
turning your arm

Evy you say

that's my daughter

I sketched it myself

both of us are startled
to find me bending down

to kiss the tattoo

*

the third time I see you naked

I get a gash on my forehead
from a barbwire fence

when we squeeze into a shed
for storing yard waste

then it rains

semen blood summer drizzle

*

what did you do to your forehead?

get out your readings I say

my homeroom students ask lots of questions:

do you have any kids?
are you married?
where do you live?
you go out on the town?
have you got a boyfriend?

I say:

I live in Amager

the students have clandestine conversations
on Facebook during class

suddenly they all smile at the same time

I don't know if it's because of me

something I've said

my clothes

a gob of spit flies from my mouth
as I stand by my desk and discuss

the essay genre

I pretend to ignore it
and keep talking

while I replay in my head
the gob in slo-mo

*

students aren't permitted in here

the janitor stands in the door to the copy room

I'm a teacher I say
and show him my ID

he looks at it for a long time

remember to clean up after yourself he says

*

I distribute welcome leaflets to the parents

they sit at the student desks

the students sit in the windowsills

there's cake and coffee
if you're into that sort of thing

STAR makes a sweeping gesture

he's like a fish in water

he's thirty-five and wearing a tweed jacket

it gives me authority he laughed
when we were fetching the extra chairs

I explain about the book depot

the smoking policy

Danish class

when the parents ask questions
they only look at STAR

he explains about student counseling

the intro trip

the assignment oasis

or more colloquially:

the homework dungeon

the parents laugh

he moves on to the class trip

we'll go in November

the Colosseum

the food

the Roman metro

the eyes

the noses

the various ways of sitting

I try to figure out how students
and parents fit together

I try to understand that the students

are somebody's kids

*

can you grab me those hearts?

my sister futzes with the glue stick

she lives in Valby

she goes to med school
and is a year and a half younger

how far have you got with the names?

we're getting there I say

the place cards are for November

Thomas is a chef

he put the ring in a pastry shell

do you want mother of the bride and father of the bride
or just their names? I ask

no damn idea

Thomas! she yells out to the kitchen

no their names she says then

never mind! she yells

and peels the plastic from a gold marker

well how's it going with the teaching?

she asks without glancing up

she puts the cap back on the marker
sets the paper down and cocks her head
like when she was a girl

I think it's hard I say

sometimes I just can't understand
how it happened

what?

that I'm somebody's teacher

she looks up and laughs

I'm not trying to be funny I say

don't you feel that way
about being somebody's doctor?

nah she says

that's just the way it is

hey what did you do to your forehead?

she leans in across the table

I push my chair back

I biked into a branch on the way to Central Station

want me to look at it?

no it's fine

I rearrange the bangs over my brow

apple cider and cookies says Thomas
stepping into the living room with a tray

he bows deep before us

from Discovery cultivars

unfiltered

thanks I say and take a glass

how goes with the commute? he asks

well it's actually not too bad

*

your hand

in a square of light

the sun casts through the train window

*

it was right there

you point out the window

her name was Martha

we're someplace in Høje-Taastrup

once you wrote
the name of your high school girlfriend

in graffiti along the tracks

of course it was painted over long ago you say

but I always look anyway

I leaf through your sketchbook
while you're in the toilet

I write my name
on one of the pages with your pencil
and rub it out again

*

last period

maybe the last summer day

the kids are playing *rundbold*
Danish softball

the best thing about being an adult is
I don't have to take part

Otto P and Otto S

Signe Sandra Villads

I sit on a bench and practice names

Clara Klara Noah

and keep an eye on the smartphones

you're out

no I was midair

Otto P and Otto S strip off their T-shirts

I think of hard nectarines

they still play that a homer gives an extra out

a bird flies across the field

Klara ducks

then glances quickly about

once a girl from the other class in my grade
caught the ball by chance

in the hollow of her elbow

while she stood in the outfield chilling

hands behind her head
eyes shut
and face tipped toward the sun

people come in close
and cup their hands together
when a poor player steps to the plate

there's the flat bat and the round bat

no no use the flat one dammit
yells Otto P at Klara

hey I say

without anyone hearing me

hey

*

I'm wearing the same dress

as Sandra

*

the shopping cart's humongous

everything huge
in this Bilka

I'm responsible for the intro trip shopping

walking up and down the aisles
and packing the cart with goods

like a single mom with twenty-five kids

I try to figure out how much milk
we need

and what it means when it says

spray

on the list

were you thinking of biking in jeans?

BROM looks me up and down
next morning in the parking lot

it's twenty miles

and what about a helmet?

we really ought to set an example

she's got ten classes of gym each week

she's fully decked out

gloves and cleated shoes

she turns around and claps her hands

I take up the rear with EMO

I bought mine last year

she points to her helmet

it's got a camouflage pattern

she's tied her skirt up around her knees

her chain rattles a little

BROM's in front
along with the students on racing bikes

they're unpacking when we arrive

the students will sleep in tents

the teachers in a cabin

everyone's going to share showers and toilets

so I won't shit for three days

such an oppressive
humid heat

Otto P and Otto S spread out a tarp
and get permission to fetch the hose

waterslide in underwear

the ones who don't want to join in
stand in knots and watch

star run later

but the longest line of clothing game
alcohol

and cucumber relays are forbidden

BROM goes out to check on them

the students are supposed to make dinner over the fire

Sandra's group is grilling chicken fillets

the rest order pizza

BROM's taking care of the teachers' food

it's delivered by her husband in styrofoam boxes

Norway lobster and cod soup

I'd rather have pizza

I've brought two bottles of wine to share
but don't dare take them out of my bag

a midnight round with flashlights

I don't like shining the beam on students

BROM douses a campfire

she's in a long black raincoat

I can maybe smell hash
but don't say anything to the others

it looks fun out in the tents

I walk in among some bushes
and light a cigarette

we're standing on the beach
at camp in eighth grade

no wind

then we see rain on the horizon

it sets the surface of the sea in motion

a long sough on its way to us

I am thirteen and I think:

here comes life

cloudburst around three

Klara and Clara are the first to come running
in bare legs and rubber boots

sleeping bags and pads over their heads

then the rest come tumbling

I stand at the cabin door

and make that
gesture with my arm

shovel them in

they bump tables and chairs about

they jostle around on the floor of the living room

BROM whistles and I say

everybody just simmer down

I lie in my room
listen to the students' voices

I can't sleep

are you lying with your wife whispering
in your bedroom in the dark?

I can't sleep
while you lie there and whisper

*

it's blustery in Ringsted

we're standing with our heads
close together in the park

trying to light our cigarettes

I'm thinking of that photo
of Queen Margrethe and Prince Henrik
when they're standing just like this

symmetrically

and are so marvelously
young and enamored

I feel like I'm in a dream you say
and your cigarette catches

good or bad?

I'm not exactly sure

I wish we'd met each other
ten years ago I say

you blow smoke and shake your head

then Evy wouldn't have been born

on the way to the station you get hungry

no thanks I say

you come out of the grill with two burgers
and hold out one to me

it's so boring to eat alone

you smile

I get a sudden urge to rub the burger
in your face

and don't know why I just
say thank you and eat it

*

the fourth time I see you naked

the train's at a standstill

because someone's been run over
on some other stretch of track

that gives us more time you say
and lift me up
next to the sink

I touch your hair
and find myself thinking of

your head

detached from your body

September

*

your wife is smiling

she's got wide lips

an oval face

she's rather beautiful

or maybe it's just a lucky shot

I'm afraid I'll accidentally like it

one profile pic no cover pic

married to and birthdate

that's all I can see

she's born in '79

she's got 335 friends

that's fewer than me

on the other hand
one of them is you

she likes local organic produce

music I don't know

graphic designers and galleries same as you

I scroll up and down

and think of all you share
that I cannot see

you stand beneath a yellow umbrella
in line before the Colosseum

rain droplets on the lens

you gaze at the photographer

your profile photo must be ten years old

maybe it's your wife who took it

you look happy

I get a friend request
and think for a second it's you

it takes some time before I realize
who Noah is

I delete it

then go to his profile page

look at his photos

just look at yourselves!

you're all so fleshy!

that's what my history teacher shouted in class one day
and everyone burst out laughing

he set off the alarm
at Museum Silkeborg
because he accidentally touched

the glass case with the Tollund Man

Noah stands spotlit on stage in a kimono

I imagine his face in ten years

twenty

he's on his way up a mountain with a backpack
and looks back at the person taking the picture

then he suddenly pokes me

I don't know how to take it

I had a crush on my physics teacher Stephanie

she always drank iced tea and smelled of chewing gum

she got lamps to light up

a marshmallow to expand in a bell jar

a gummy bear to swell up in a glass of water

one day the sun will explode
she said at the end of one period

or simply burn out

then I was no longer in love with her

Frederik from my class in grade school

in the cottage
another kid on his lap

I can remember his birthday

the number of his parents' landline

he got chewed out
because he was a terrible Secret Santa

didn't give anything before the twentieth

now he's somebody's dad

I can remember all sorts of episodes

voices

handwriting styles

Anna's

those hands
Anna had

they're thin and dry

little fingertips

that tickle when she braids my hair

she's good at drawing
but holds the pencil wrong

the Danish teacher

twists a grooved red rubber triangle
down over it

it's hard on the fingers

we peel it off

and then that completely crazy drawing on ledger paper
of the dragons

the paper shiny with crayon

Anna Anna

what are you doing *right now*?

*

each lesson is constructed on the ROPES model

STAR points at his screen

Review Overview Presentation Exercise Summary

relax

it'll feel like old hat next year
when you do your postgrad training

he's giving me his teaching materials
for a sociolinguistics and grammar unit

I've spiced up my powerpoints a bit he says

with pictures and memes

it's important to have something visual
if you want them to listen

and then I thought

he reaches down in his bag

you might want to take a gander

he smacks a book onto the desk

at this

good grief I say and pick it up

High School Pedagogy – A Primer

I weigh it in my hand and riffle through

753 pages

he's stuck in sticky notes
of different colors

dig in he says and laughs

for those long dark nights

*

Noah

I say three times during the next period

but he just stretches

*

the students almost all make
the same mistake

flush out instead of flesh out

I've made a funny PowerPoint
a picture of a toilet
with an X across it

you don't flush out an argument
you flesh it out

you don't flush it out
you flesh it out

going home on the train I think

what a load of crock to stand there and say

*

the fifth time I see you naked:

my bedroom

even though it's risky

but we don't dare stay on the train

and it's become too cold to be outside

you shower before you go
so you don't carry my smell home

I sniff the towel afterward

*

the sixth time I see you naked:

my bedroom

I lie down on the bed

afterward

beside the pillow
you mashed flat

*

I try not to think about

your wife's naked body

*

your wife's naked body

*

I'm not sure why neither of us
says her name

don't you think I know what she's called?

*

the seventh time I see you naked:

my kitchen

morning

such a weird light
when you've left

and a scent of something sweet
from the bag on the table

you brought cake

a cock a cake a brain a heart
you brought

and left behind the cake

*

I put the kettle on

lie down on the kitchen floor

I come before it boils

*
Maria

*

and now there's only 171 schooldays till summer vacation

FLIB places his bag on the desk
and steps out of his shoes

he counts down every morning

last year his senior class won
two national prizes

best audio and best script

for their final film in media studies

a clipping from the local paper
on the bulletin board in the teachers' lounge

with a photo of FLIB
being thrown in the air by students

so there's only twelve years till retirement
he said recently

give it a rest already

KILI threw an apple at him

you couldn't live without this place

she always seems super stressed

she teaches English
with a pronounced British accent

students aren't allowed to speak Danish in her classes

FLIB changes into Chinese slippers and boots up his laptop

he doesn't use a school Acer but his own Mac

his teaching's very computer-based

of course that's something the administration loves
KILI tells me over lunch

*

the chicken lays an egg
the egg lies in the nest

I've written that on the board

Noah raises his hand

to lay is to place
to lie's to recline

that's how I learned it he says

to lay is to place
to lie's to recline

exactly I say

and think of my math teacher
who went around among the desks

knees bent crouching

and snapped her fingers while she sang

divide multiply subtract and bring down
divide multiply subtract and bring down

I start laughing at my desk

why's that funny? asks Sandra

she's got beautiful eyes

perhaps a bit bulgy

she always sits in the front row
together with Christina and Noah

well it isn't really
I say and cough

they can't hear I've got a lozenge in my cheek

a common fear among the younger teachers

I think again of my math teacher

putrefaction and death

STAR's got a pack of V6 on his desk

EMO's always eating Mentos

*

where do you see this in the text?

beware of name symbolism

fine with the eight potatoes

wrong tense

what?

do more with the axe

where do you see this in the text?

beware of name symbolism

fine with the eight potatoes

wrong tense

what?

do more with the axe

I could copy and paste my comments

when I'm finished I have the urge
to wipe En Flinker Fyr by Pia Juul

clean again

there are certain things you must never give them
MIRG said to me

she's taught Danish for forty years

the things you hold dearest
you must keep to yourself

*

when you correct our essays
would you mind actually using

the Latin terms? Sandra asks

that's what we use in our other subjects

*

somebody gets a text

from now on all of you please
put your phones on mute

they get going on the group work

I discover it was me

you've sent a link
to Under Your Spell

and written

I think I'm in love with you

*

shit says Villads

when I explain that most people
took notes by hand when I was in high school

he photographs the board with his phone

I take the eraser when the students have left
but my notes won't wipe away

the marker isn't meant for whiteboards

I take a step backward

we've been working with obscenity
invective and slang

in the middle it says in big letters

CUM DUMPSTER

*

your phone rings

while you're telling me about a street artist
you once met in Nepal

it's Maria

you turn your head away
yet I can hear her voice clearly

there are problems with Evy

she doesn't want to be dropped off

now the kindergarten's called

you scoot all the way over to the window

I go to the train toilet
and look at myself in the mirror

I am Maria

Evy's clinging to me

her arms around my neck

the teacher twisting them free
and pulling her tight

Evy shrieking and kicking

reaching out to me

now now says the teacher

she nods to the door
and tries to restrain Evy's legs

now now yes yes

she mimes to me over Evy's head

you need to leave now

I walk across the gravel

pull my jacket snug around me

not looking back

I sit in the car not driving

clench and unclench my fists

someone tries the handle

I flush the toilet

it's impossible to go back to the street artist

want to split a muesli bar? I ask

no thanks

you're looking out the window

she sometimes gets these

attacks of homesickness you say

it was really awful last spring
when she was at camp

ahh

I want to say more

but I cannot
talk to you about her

I cannot
know anything about her

it feels as though I'm taking
something that isn't mine

*

the next morning you aren't on the platform

I get a text when I'm sitting in the train

kid sick

I reply

get well soon

you reply

you can't write me
I'll write you

*

Evy's lying in the top bunk
and moving her legs in her sleeping bag

she sighs loudly

turns so the slats creak

listens

the others don't wake up

their breathing in the dark

she stares at the strip of light from the door

the counselors' voices from the common room
stopped a long time ago

under her pillow's a postcard
with a picture of a polar bear family

that you've drawn

Maria's handwriting on the back

Evy's had them read it out loud twice

she pulls the sleeping bag up all the way over her head

then kicks it off

the weeping moves up through her throat

close your eyes Evy

imagine your eyelids
are heavy doors

as long as you keep them shut
the homesickness can't get you

think of oranges

think of a fat bunny

think of a big ship
gliding into port

and the sea is orange

at some point it'll be morning

*

the eighth time I see you naked:

my bedroom

I stand at the window afterward
and watch you walk your bike through the courtyard

the empty child's seat

as if a ghost rides behind

October

*

two brothers

tie a boy from the road to the kitchen table
and saw his leg off with a fretsaw

it's a laborious process

it's my Danish teacher
who reads these enormities aloud

while she sits at her desk
and taps her foot

I'm ten and faint onto the linoleum floor

I'm bored by language and grammar
so I've decided to start a unit

on horror

I don't know how impressionable the students are

it turns out that the twin girls
are the only ones they find spooky
in The Shining

they think Wendy looks weird
and laugh when the chef gets killed with an axe

old films are generally a bit comical says Otto S

Sandra says new films are scarier

because it's easier to identify
with people who look like you

*

in a glass cabinet in the bedroom
the man's dead wife is displayed

embalmed

with diamonds in her eye sockets

that's the setup in the Ingemann story
I've assigned the students to analyze

Christina talks about the woman
as a symbol of drive and sexuality

Sandra says the man
has locked his passion away behind glass

some of the students have trouble with the language

it's crazy old says Villads

I have to make a glossary

gloat: to be smug about your success or another's misfortune

embalm: to prepare a dead body to keep it from rotting

sapphire: a precious blue stone

*

I'm feeling a bit dizzy you say

the ninth time I see you naked

on your way out you walk into the glass
in front of the elevator in my building

your forehead leaves

a greasy print

*

Maria touches the bump carefully

she wraps a dishtowel around
a bag of frozen peas

*

the doorbell's ringing

a girl scout's standing outside

while the woman talks to her
we see something moving
up through the drainpipe under the sink

it's suspense says Noah

because we know more than her

I'm using the short film Kitchen Sink
to introduce Freud and repression

the woman hauls a hairy
fetal creature up from the drain

ooh gross says Klara
and turns her head away

the woman puts the monster in her bathtub

it grows and develops into a man
whom she drags into the bedroom

she shaves his body

dresses him in fine clothes
and lays him in her bed

the entire class wails when he wakens
and they begin to kiss

Noah comes up to my desk after class

you really remind me of
someone or other when you talk

and your hair

and just that way
you move your hands

well I say
and gather up my papers

who?

I don't know he says

maybe someone from a film

he pulls off his hood
and puts it up again

I don't know what to say

we turn our heads in tandem

Otto P and Otto S
are trying to do handstands against the end wall

*

looking rather cool today

the mother smiles as we pass each other in the entry port

she carries a boy in her arms

there's a kindergarten
on the ground floor of my building

it's early in the morning

perhaps she thinks that I'm also
just dropping off a kid

thank you I say and feel happy
I put on this hat

on the train it strikes me that

she was talking about the weather

*

there are lanterns in the bushes when I get home

the teachers have organized a candle party

kindergartners and parents joining hands

they walk in procession

I go up to my apartment

station myself by the window
without removing my coat

prop the window open

I walk with my lantern
my lantern walks with me

a tureen rests on one of the benches

perhaps they've had soup

up there shine the stars
down here shine we

they walk round and round the backyard
singing the same four lines

over and over again

I light a cigarette

then the lantern man appears behind a bush

it's a teacher with a pillow on her belly

beard and cane

some of the kids start to cry

the parents pacify them

the lantern man hands out apples from his sack

the candles the kids the apples

the whole thing makes me quite sad

*

it's become darker in the mornings

but on the other hand:

wild sunrises through the train window

you kiss me although I have a cold

my germs spill into you
and then into Evy and Maria

next week all three of you are sick

the theme is angels and demons

the assembly hall's decorated with a red carpet

tulle around the columns

black balloons

there are sandwiches and earplugs in the teachers' lounge

FLIB's wearing a shirt with flames

he's purchased plastic horns

and brought shoe polish
for painting goatees

you completely sure?

he extends a pair of horns to KILI

she inserts her earplugs

you may as well go for broke he tells me

we have the first bar watch together

can you handle it lads?
he asks as he pulls them pints

everyone wants to be served by him
and borrow his horns
and include him in their selfies

I try to look busy

wipe the counter clean

restock the fridge

color-coordinate Breezers

Otto P Otto S and Villads
enter single file

torsos naked

angel wings

they stare straight at me

a beer pong set says Otto P

can I try these?

he reaches for my horns

nope I say jerking my head back

Otto S hops onto the bar

aren't you going to join us?

ha ha I say

I take pains not to let
the beers foam when I pour

how fast can you chug one of these?

ha ha I say again
and drop two ping-pong balls

my face feels stiff

maybe it's the shoe polish

good that the music's loud

then I return his glance

faster than you I say

later Christina and Sandra buy Somersbys

they're wearing identical blue dresses
knee socks and stilettos

The Shining says Sandra

Noah arrives late

with a girl I don't know
wearing cat ears and whiskers

red dress

it's very tight

he's got a Scream mask around his neck

his hand resting upon her hip
as they walk to the bar

two green Breezers she shouts
and leans all the way across the counter

her breath smells sweet and a bit yeasty

her eyes swimming

she's pale beneath her makeup

think that's a good idea?

I could ask

or simply give her a cola

she fumbles with MobilePay

I watch them as they leave

the girl rocking her hips to the music
holding the Breezer in front of her

I walk over to the dance floor when my shift ends

it's packed

neon-colored smoke

I try to distinguish the bodies from each other

it feels strange to be sober

like walking around in another person's dream

my body feels restless

I place myself up against a column
and shove my hands in my pockets

move my fingers down there in time to the beat

it thumps in my ribcage

then Otto P and Otto S come running toward me

their wings jumping

they grab my wrists and drag me away

no no no I shout
and vote against them with my feet

then we're in the middle of the floor

they swing my arms to get me to dance

I let them flop

then suddenly I make a series of totally wild moves

they howl with enthusiasm

I shove my way out from among the dancing bodies

EMO stands leaning against the wall
a garland of angel hair around her head

she's got a dead look on her face

she stares at her phone
and returns it to her pocket

I want to go over to her

but someone touches my arm

it's Noah

can you just come with me? he shouts

the girl stands leaning over the sink

it looks insane

in some way beautiful

the screaming green puke
against the red dress

hey I say

and go over and place my arm around her shoulders

honey

she raises her head

the light is bright

our faces in the mirror

her whiskers

my goatee

get EMO I say to Noah

he turns around and
the Scream mask stares at me

when the girl's father arrives
she's sitting leaning up against me
on the floor of the teachers' lounge

the back of her head against my chest

I'm stroking her forehead with my thumb

EMO's squatting with a water bottle

the girl's cat ears in her other hand

I'm so very sorry the father says

we help him maneuver her into the car

her head dangling

I'm so extremely sorry

don't worry about it I say
and EMO passes him the ears

it happens

*

on Wednesday during fall vacation I run into Noah
at the World Press Photo exhibition

at Politikens Hus

I get flustered
seeing him outside school

and find myself hugging him

before a photo of a large orangutan
on an operating table

afterward I shake the hands of his parents

*

two people who love each other

dear Thomas dear Sis

beautiful people

I sit in the sunroom not getting anywhere with my speech

I can see my parents through the glass door

they're standing facing each other on the living room floor
and performing a dance:

stretch shake stretch together
stretch shake stretch together

the bed linen's white

my dad is tall

my mom short

if he extends an arm
horizontally
she can just stand under it

Stendyssevej 1

Smedelinjen 45

I'm looking at different summer cottages on Røsnæs

Northwest Zealand

the three of you will be away all week

it's about sixty miles from Copenhagen

have you even talked to anyone from your building?
asks my mom while we make food

what do you mean?

I'm spinning lettuce

well there might be

my mom wrings out a dishrag

a nice neighbor or something

it'd be good for you to settle down
she once told me

and both of us screamed

because I accidentally threw a pair of scissors
I was holding in my hand

she was so happy the day I called
and told her I'd landed the job in Næstved

and the commute time you can of course think of
as office time said my dad

there's a lot you can do in an hour each way

my mom wipes the dining table

no I say

that's not the way it works

I don't even know what my neighbors look like

well what do I know

she shakes out the rag in the sink

I go out to the bathroom and text my sister:

I miss you

she doesn't reply

she's on Funen with all her in-laws

maybe they've gone to the beach in the wind

she's borrowed a fleece from Thomas's mother

now she's got a nephew on her lap

she's reading out loud
and brushing her hair behind her ear

the nephew stroking the sleeves of her sweater

with or without? asks my mom

there are big chocolate-covered marshmallows after dinner

my dad likes those with coconut best
my mom likes those without

they've bought a package with three of each

you two can just split them

I go down to the basement for the extra cot

haul it up the stairs

my dad makes up a bed in the office
which once was my room

my mother's breasts
when she washes herself in the bathroom

time speaks to me
through them

*

you can't figure out
where the fruit flies are coming from

they swarm around the dishrag in the cottage kitchen

they rise from the sink when you turn on the tap

fruit flies lay eggs in rotten fruit
yet the oranges are fresh and in the fridge

eww yells Evy excited

Maria finds a rotten pear
in the cabinet beneath the sink

she sticks a hand in a freezer bag
and scoops up the pear

it's nearly liquid

she twists the bag around the pear
and ties a knot

can I see?

Evy puts her face right up to the bag

some flies cling to the inner surface

into the trash it goes says Maria

she walks down the driveway with the bag

something's rustling somewhere in the hedge

some birds

a cat

a hedgehog perhaps

*

early morning

the three of you in the double bed

Maria's been awake for some time

she doesn't know where her agitation comes from

she looks at Evy's eyelashes

your hand
in a square of light
the sun casts upon the mattress

it's utterly quiet

she listens to your breathing

she suddenly has the urge to scream
or throw something against the wall

listen to loud music

she gets up and goes into the living room

opens the patio door

it's chilly

your jacket hangs over the back of the couch

she puts it on
and pokes her feet into a pair of rubber boots

she sits down on a patio chair

closes her eyes

breathes deeply

the agitation doesn't sit in one part of her body

it migrates

she imagines that she's here by herself

the sun on her face

the poplars murmuring

she tries to draw that simplicity
deep into her lungs

she sticks her hands into your jacket pockets

fumbles a little
and fishes out your cigarettes

she hasn't smoked in ten years

the lighter's inside the pack

she smokes two

then she hears footfalls

someone's pacing on the gravel path behind the hedge

back and forth

she gets up

the footsteps stop

her fingers are freezing

then she goes back in and lights the oven

heats water for eggs

the kitchen drain gives off a faint smell of sewer

*

when you swing out onto Røsnæsvej

you run over a cat

Evy cries in the car the whole way home

*

hi guys I say after vacation

hi darlings hi cuties hi kids

and in the middle of second period
I accidentally call Christina Chris

I don't know where that came from

I've also begun to talk louder
and move about the classroom

the shitty email system in Lectio

I meet STAR in the teachers' lounge during my free period

he bangs his head on the table

he's written an email about Otto P
whose truancy rate has topped fifty percent

and who also possibly

has been selling ecstasy behind Bilka

instead of sending the message
to all the teachers of the class
he's sent it

to all the students of the class

he fiddles with his beard while I read

immature and maladjusted
among other things

heading for the precipice

it's not that bad I say
and pat him on the shoulder

I shudder

off to the gallows he says and stands up

I open my computer

I've got a new message

I'd actually prefer to just be called Christina

*

the baby buggy stands deserted under a tree

quiet crying

a young guy in a cap stops

goes over and lifts the blanket

the top springs open
and the baby sits up and screams

it's got red eyes
a completely twisted face

puke in a thick white stream

Devil Baby Attack is the name of the prank

can I show you something on YouTube? asked Otto P
when I came into the classroom after break

it's thematically relevant to our unit

pull yourself together Christina tells him

Sandra's sitting with her arms crossed

*

something happens in front of Fakta

I've got greasy hair

I'm wearing my glasses and sneakers

I've just been in to buy a large pack of TP
that I'm about to hang from my handlebars

the two of you are walking toward me

with the baby carriage

first your face goes white
then your face goes red

I find myself saying

hi

hi you say

hi says Maria

this is Maria you say

hi there

and this is one of the ones who is
who's also in

the running club

sometimes

you say sweeping your arm toward me

hi

and this here is Evy

*

when I get home
you've sent a text:

!

hi I say before the mirror

and take my glasses off and on

hi there

*

Maria Maria

I noticed
you have dimples

what do you think about
when you think about happiness?

I noticed
you had mittens on
even though it was mild

I freeze all the time too

maybe we could
all of us love each other?

*

Evy lies on a red mattress

I kneel and look at her

she's mumbling

then she reaches for me in her sleep

I don't dare pick her up

there's a mist around her skin

I pick her up anyway

she smells of you

then she bursts into flames

I try to put them out with my hands

my hands catch on fire

I try to stay quiet
so the other children don't wake up

they wake up

and begin to cry on their mattresses

two teachers come running

another dream:

I walk around the park carrying Evy in my arms

bob her up and down

I discover she has a leaf in her mouth

I try to pick it out with my fingers
but it's her tongue I grab hold of

it's turned into a green leaf

the skin of her face begins to turn green

then she bites down on my forefinger

her teeth are needle sharp
and she throws her head from side to side

my finger gets torn off

I shriek and the blood pours out of her mouth

at that moment I see Maria
come walking across the lawn

*

I sit facing opposite the direction of travel

and watch things disappear

November

*

the tenth time I see you naked

you meet a mother from Evy's swim class
on your way out of my courtyard

you have to invent something

you're nervous

you don't want to meet at my place anymore

we revert to the train

you tell Maria
your hours have changed

we take a very early departure

with almost no passengers
and more stops

I can't use chapstick
or scented body lotion

they leave traces on your clothes

*

you accidentally kiss me on the mouth
in the afternoon when we say goodbye

we're standing with our bikes in front of Central Station

you pull your head back with a jerk

*

I can't

that's all it reads

*

you're not on the train

I walk through all the carriages twice

I sit down with the phone in my hands

at Glumsø I call

you don't answer

I write

call

and regret

*

your phone's resting on the counter

Maria touches it and sees my text

all day long I picture the scene

Evy running into her room

*

you're not on the train

I tear pages from the railway magazine to tiny bits
and place them in patterns on the table

I sweep them into my hand at Roskilde

three young women
with two coffees to go
in almost identical coats

sit down around me

oops sorry the one says

she smiles at me and moves her foot

*

you're not on the train

that ray of sun hits me

thirteen times

can one hear on that stretch
Halo on repeat

*

you're not on the train

I walk from the station to the school

mouth open in a headwind

*

you're not on the train

I don't get off in Næstved
but continue to Nykøbing Falster

they call from school three times

I ride back to Copenhagen

Nykøbing Falster

Copenhagen

Nykøbing Falster

*

the last train pulls into Central Station

it's a bit past one a.m.

I'm alone in the carriage

the conductor making the rounds

I nod to him and stand up
put on my scarf

I take the scarf off again
and my shoes

I fold my legs under me

sit a while

a woman on the platform zips up her coat

we make eye contact through the window

she looks serene

she turns and walks toward the escalator

the lights in the train go out

I want to leave

I want to join her

but now the doors are locked

the train begins to move

I have to ring the railway's emergency number

the woman on the line bawls me out

a man in an orange vest gets me
and follows me back along the rails

what the hell were you doing? he says

I have to trot to keep up

this isn't a playground

*

smell of alcohol in the classroom

during a break BROM and KILI discuss
writing a complaint to Crazy Daisy
and asking them to discontinue

Turbo Thursdays

I have a hangover too

I sit at my desk

and look at you and Maria's apartment
on Google Street View

*

I pick up a stone
and walk around among the bikes
in front of your building

the black the green the silver

I try to figure out which one
is Maria's

I place the stone in the basket of the black bike

I walk through the entrance to the courtyard

there's a lawn

two benches

a sandbox

a swing set

it's dark

only light from a couple of windows

a creaking sound

there's someone sitting
on the one swing

I walk across the grass

hi Evy I say

she glances up

why're you sitting here?

'cause I'm waiting for you she says

aren't you freezing? I ask

she nods

I take off my coat
and help her into it

tell me about death she says

no

yes

tell me

I glance up toward your windows

the lights are off

if you die then you aren't alive I say

I don't care she says

if you're not alive you can't eat anymore
and you can't play either

that doesn't matter says Evy

'cause I'm a horse you see

if you're dead you can't be a horse either

yes but I'm really not dead she says

she points to the other swing

swing with me

I seat myself beside her

we get the swings going

start swinging in unison

my coat flapping around her

let's jump she says

okay I say

I'll count to three she says

and then you'll wake up

one

two

three

*

I'm moving in with my boyfriend

and his little girl

into a flat in Amager

Holmbladsgade

I say to the hairdresser
when she asks where

exciting she says

how old's the girl?

four

she goes to preschool

it was hard in the beginning
but now we're quite close

her mother's dead I say

so it hasn't been easy

that's really awful says the hairdresser

she holds my head fast

now you have to sit completely still
because now we're doing the bangs

outside the hairdresser Maria's waiting

I get into the stroller

she straps me in with a belt

are you comfortable? she asks
and gives me a cracker

we roll over Langebro

the sky is dark

we take the elevator down to tracks 7 and 8

she lets me press the button

you're standing on the platform

there's no other people

something's wrong

I twist around

the belt's tight

my arms short

I open my mouth
but I've got no voice

you place your hand on the handlebar

I try to catch your eye
but you won't look at me

then you give the stroller a shove

I can hear the train

*

my sister in white lace

loose hair down her back

she looks like pictures of my mom in her youth

my dad suited up at her side

they walk down the aisle

I can see her before me on her knees

in satin and platform shoes
at her confirmation

bad skin

and the minister's got a bubble in his throat

it sounds weird when he speaks

my sister glances at me from up by the altar

we start to laugh

we can't stop

the other confirmands shift uneasily

the minister reddens and coughs

my dad pinches my arm hard

he chews us out on the way to the party

my sister removes her sparkly barrettes
and hides behind her bangs

there's nothing I'd rather do says Thomas

my sister cries

then Thomas cries too

and my dad

thank you for the shining day that is departed

I don't know the melody

my mom takes my hand

there's something in my mouth

I don't know if it's sobs
or a hysterical laugh

It's freezing out in front of the church

my uncle throws rice at me for fun

I've an urge to spike him with my heel

everybody swivel a bit shouts the photographer

so that you turn toward the bride

smile ladies

lovely

then we'll take one where you wave

yes

you with the feathers

can you take them out or place yourself on the outside?

fine

tongue against palate

long neck

cheese

and now with a bit more passion

the scallops are hard to get down

their consistency

don't you want the last one?

my uncle spears the scallop with his fork

his jaw muscles when he chews

we clink the silverware

Thomas helps my sister up

they kiss standing on their chairs

first cautiously

then French and everybody hoots

I think of black slugs mating

I fill my glass with white wine

and I love your hair and your smile
you find the woods and you find
me lying among stars
we never can reach

I end my toast by reading a poem
from *My Inner Pompeii*

and I'm amazed
that my voice is so steady

and I love
your laughter and the confused desert
you have in your gaze

Thomas blinks fiercely as I read

my sister hugs me for a long time afterward

I feel like Judas

beef tenderloin
with Bordelaise sauce and crisp carrots

one half of the song sheets are in a cast iron pan

now we shall go with a heart so red

heart so red

heart so red

we file past the newlyweds
each of us with a heart-shaped sticker

in the end their faces are completely covered

I can't get it to stop
looking like a rash

boils or chickenpox

everyone's taking pictures

lemon sorbet
with ginger and mint leaves

open bar and petit fours

well and what about you then?

the photographer plants his elbow on the counter of the bar

he's one of Thomas's friends

is that a fish skeleton?

I point to a tattoo on his forearm

he's rolled up his sleeves

it's the different parts of a camera lens

he continues to look at me

what about you then? he asks again

I can see Thomas leaning into my sister
and then they both glance over at us

yeah what about me?

nice toast he says

are you an author?

I'm a teacher I say

the wedding cake has five layers

Thomas developed the recipe
and my sister did the taste-testing

the photographer wants to dance with me after

he's taken his shoes off
and moves his hips a lot

I try to step on his toes

I need to tell you something
I shout into my sister's hair
on the dance floor around two

I'm totally out of it!

what are you saying? she yells

but then Superstition comes on
and we spill our drinks
because my aunt jostles us with her hip

I plant my forehead against the mirror out in the bathroom

stand that way a long time

till I get a text

something important
or at least weird

I met your name-double today
at the flea market

I bought three pigs in a blanket
from an older woman with MobilePay

and when I'd entered her number
it was your name that popped up

both first and last

what are the odds?

I miss you

I barely make it to the toilet bowl in time:

wedding cake
lemon sorbet
beef tenderloin
scallops

*

marry me I whisper

the eleventh time I see you naked

*

what's he want?

my sister's eyes dart around

he doesn't know I say

because of Evy

his daughter

he doesn't want to hurt her

oh Jesus

my sister sets a mandoline slicer down on the coffee table
and bangs her screen shut

we've been making lists of the gifts

she looks at me

I know I know I say

it's a real mess

but it's my body

it's like it only exists
when it touches his

the rest of the time I'm this haze drifting about

you're not a haze

my sister grasps me by the shoulders

and besides you could have that with somebody else

no I say

I can't

yes you can

no

we sit for a time

well but then you have to say to him

you're serious about the whole nine yards

also being a stepmother

if that's really what you want?

that's really what I want

she stares at the mandoline

if it were Thomas

I get to my feet

I knew you would say that
but it isn't

and life can't be that way for everyone

you and Thomas

Mom and Dad

it's just not like that for everyone

because people are egotistical she says
and expect too much of each other

because they're bored

because they give up

or because they fall in love I say

infatuations fade

*

before Christmas

you say

before Christmas

*

a woman gazes demonically out at the viewer
while she holds her newborn triplets
by their umbilical cords

a man pisses on the floor
and stares at a skull that resembles
his own face

they're standing in a room with patterned wallpaper

the composition symmetrical

oil on canvas

got to really be a sick brain
to make stuff like this says Otto P

and who's going to hang it on their walls?

Klara knits her brow

it's deliberately repellent

Sandra talks about death
and dysfunctionality
in the nuclear family

skull egg lemon

Christina reads aloud from an online article

Kvium's symbols remind us that
a person's days are numbered

I relate an anecdote
about Kvium's portrait
of Queen Margrethe

the level of detail is spooky

almost like a photograph

the wrinkles

and Margrethe's one eye
that's just a touch lazy

at the opening she looks a long time first at the painting

and then at Kvium and says

thou hast captured truly everything

the students laugh

I feel giddy

but down in the teachers' lounge I realize
it's not Kvium at all

who painted that picture

but Thomas Kluge

*

the vaulted ceiling of Termini Station
resembles enormous ribs

as if we're wandering about inside the ribcage of a whale

STAR distributes metro maps

I count students

I can feel my heart the entire time

it's swollen up

fifteen degrees Celsius and November sun

we dump our coats

Hotel Madonna

STAR speaks Italian with the desk clerk

he's nearly fluent

he lived two years in Rome when he studied history

the students struggle with their luggage

and for you says the clerk

the key to my room dangles between his fingers

professoressa

he smiles

he's got steel-frame spectacles

a double bed

green walls

thin curtains in front of the window
facing onto the street

that's what my lodgings are like

the students in six-person rooms on either side

at night I'm anxious
there'll be a knock on the door

that someone'll need help

I lie and gaze out into the darkness

nothing happens

occasionally I hear laughter through the walls

I run into Klara in the hallway in the morning
wrapped in a towel

she's borrowed the boys' shower

her hair dripping down her back

artificial yellow juice

toast

jam

cornflakes you get from a sort of candy dispenser

whole milk in glass pitchers

the boys eat and eat

a half hour later they buy
pizza and panini from a street stand

have you been to Rome before?

I take up the rear with Noah

no I say

have you?

with my folks once

you've met them

he laughs

the traffic is insane

I think of stepping into the street and getting run over

I think of water boiling and vanishing

the students take pictures of the view from the Palatine Hill

yes whatcha think

STAR makes a sweeping gesture
as though he's showing us around his home

in the spring the orange trees smell
utterly fantastic

it starts to rain
in the line in front of the Colosseum

how long we going to stand here? asks Villads

STAR stands a little further off
talking to one of the guards

just look at it

I point at the building

isn't it simply massive?

Klara glances at me grumpily and pulls up her hood

rests her head upon Noah's shoulder

down in the underground passages
the gladiators would sit and wait I say

they'd eat their last meal

which was the meat from the animals
who'd been killed the day before

I don't know if that's true
but it seems likely

there were also systems of hoists
that could pick up the animals
and throw them into the arena

elephants and lions

hyenas I say

and once they held a naval battle Maria says
where they filled the entire Colosseum with water

you're kissing her under a yellow umbrella
you just bought from a street vendor

you're wearing a T-shirt

Maria's shoes are soaked

but you don't care about the rain

the waiting line

you've known each other two months

you're in love

Roma amor

Maria gets her camera out of her bag

she steps out of line in the rain
and raises the camera to her eye

look over here!

I point to the metro map
and show where we're getting off

the kids squeeze into the carriage

we're standing much too close

our coats dripping

a strange man presses his belly against my back

I close my eyes
and imagine he's you

I open my eyes
and catch Noah's eye in the middle of the carriage

he's grasping a bar near the ceiling

waves to me with his pinkie

an unbearable itch in my vaginal opening
materializes on our third day

the foreign bacteria in the water
have given me a yeast infection

peace and quiet

the woman at the pharmacy gives me a thick white cream

I rub it in
in a café toilet on Piazza Navona

while the kids buy cokes and club sandwiches
for their hangovers

they smoke in knots in front of the Pantheon

the rain's stopped

the diameter of the cupola is precisely the same
as its height

and the height of the cupola is precisely one half
of the temple's overall height

STAR tells me

and the holes in the floor collect rainwater
and discharge it into the Tiber

yeah I saw that in the guidebook I say

the diameter of the cupola is precisely the same
as its height

and the height of the cupola is precisely one half
of the temple's overall height

I say to Sandra and Christina

and the holes in the floor collect rainwater
and discharge it into the Tiber

we walk across one of the bridges

the water is greyish green

turbid

I go last
and listen to the students

an inside lingo

the nicknames they've given each other

I imagine the situations
that gave rise to the names

you two should be in the shot says Villads

the students have bought selfie sticks

he puts his arm around me and STAR

a Danish guide with a ponytail
shows us around the Vatican

we're connected to him via earpieces

STAR walks in front next to the guide
and sometimes adds something into the mike

my pelvic region stings

the students yawn and scuffle

they sit leaning against each other
along the walls in the Sistine Chapel

Klara on Noah's lap

no sit properly I whisper to her

Margherita pizza
and a draft pint apiece
for the shared evening meal

loud music

and poor acoustics so that everyone yells

a waiter stirs pasta
in a hollowed-out wheel of pecorino

my face has mutated into Villads's

Villads's face into mine

Otto P has done a faceswap with the photo from today

it looks monstrous

the students vanish
in all directions after dinner

wine and vodka in their bags

STAR and I buy cherry gelato by the Trevi Fountain

it's lit up like a swimming pool

down there and to the left

STAR is pointing down a narrow alley

it was a microscopic flat
and I lived with this guy from Germany

who smoked and had psoriasis

so he scratched a lot at night

you know that sound of someone's nails

and the whole flat was littered with skin flakes and pot

STAR chortles

ugh those were the days

a whiff of shampoo
when Christina and Sandra pass
in the hotel foyer

their arms wrapped around each other's waist

silver jewelry

hair down

they're heading out

I go up to my room

sit down on the edge of the bed

girls you walk in the night

the stars are children's eyes

among the cobbles sprout
death's anemones

I don't know where I got those lines from

they play on repeat

I scratch my crotch through my underwear

stripes of light on the green wall

you draw the curtains before the open window

push Maria down onto the bed

cars whooshing past

fragments of conversation in Italian

a bottle shatters against the asphalt

Maria kisses your hands

your fingers one by one

afterward the sounds from the street subside

she falls asleep on her stomach

you wipe semen off with the sheet

drape an arm across her
and slide into her dream

I light the cigarette in front of the hotel

it's three in the morning

it's chilly

my shirt is much too thin

I saw you from my room says Noah

can I bum one?

I light it for him

a taxi drives past

a siren in the distance

want to borrow this?

he unzips his jacket

no thanks

we smoke next to each other for

two

three

four minutes

hey he says
and flicks the butt into the middle of the street

you're a good teacher

then he turns around
and takes the steps in one bound

I remain standing there till I start to shiver

the desk clerk looks up from his phone
when I step into the foyer

he blows on my nipples
before he enters me

it hurts
but also feels good

like digging at a mosquito bite

I hope he doesn't notice the white cream

I remove his spectacles

please I whisper

without knowing what it is
I want him to do

December

*

the mornings are utterly dark

the only thing we can see in the window is our own faces

and Christmas lights

as we pass through station towns

*

Noah needs help
analyzing the cat

I sit down next to him

the class is reading Edgar Allan Poe

a man loves his cat
but it turns out to be evil

he kills it

but it comes back from the dead
and drives the man insane

until finally he murders his wife with an axe
and bricks her up in a wall

Noah scrolls through the pages

well off the bat I'm thinking
maybe Freud? he says

his shirt is made of some

synthetic material

that makes the hairs on my arm

stand up

*

he's cute

I look down in the baby buggy
and try to find something else to say

he's really cute

it's the first time I've met GIAN
who's on a maternity visit

she's got red cheeks
and bags under her eyes

we're standing in a semicircle around her and the buggy

everyone's gazing at the boy
who peeks up from his blanket

BROM pulls faces

LUST places a hand on the handlebar

one completely forgets how tiny they are

then she shifts her hand to GIAN's arm

now don't forget to savor it

LUST has a daughter
who's in Australia on exchange

she reads her daughter's emails to the rest of us during breaks they're group emails and quite brief

well I'm going to take the plunge

BROM reaches down into the buggy

the baby sits on her arm looking bewildered

then he's handed round

he's heavier than I expected

and rather warm

he smells sweet
of oatmeal and sugar

milk

I'm hungry and dizzy

the crania are open in infants

they're soft in any case

I'm suddenly scared of dropping him by accident

or hurling him into the wall
in some sort of fit

biting one of his fingers off

quickly I pass him on

well I've got a couple essays

I shake GIAN's hand

of course she says and smiles

we're leaving soon too

she gives my hand a squeeze

nice to meet some of the new blood

I watch her through the window
when she's said her goodbyes

she wraps a scarf around her neck

adjusts the folding top

then she pushes the buggy across the parking lot

the sun hanging low over Bilka

that night I grow anxious about whether
I might have given the baby something

I google baby + colds

baby + contagious

I find GIAN on Facebook
to see if she's written anything

about a sick child

no no just relax

my sister laughs on the phone

have you gone completely round the bend?

*

the twelfth time I see you naked

you come in my mouth

and leave to go see

Evy in a Lucia parade

*

this vertigo
that won't dissipate

I pour powdered sugar in a bowl

my sister turns the fried dough with a fork

Advent hygge

and then I look over at him
and his head is simply in flames

my mom's voice from the living room

the story of my dad's wild hair in the '70s
and an Advent wreath hanging from the ceiling

Thomas guffaws

he's heard it before says my sister
and turns down the burner

anyway

she turns to face me

you mustn't tell anyone

but after New Year's we thought we'd get started

that is we'll try

wow that's crazy

or wonderful

I give her a hug

that's wonderful

my palms begin to burn
as we sit around the table weaving paper stars

I have to go down to the street
and place them on the asphalt

you all right?

two teenagers

each with an arm around the other
each walking a bike

pull up short

yeah totally all right thanks

sure?

totally sure thank you

they smile and continue
down the street in step

I sit down on the curb
and close my eyes

Evy's eyelashes

your hands

Maria's heart

something hot surging within

I don't know if I'm going to weep
or puke

*

I shake the teacher's hand

it's my first time picking her up I say

Evy's sitting in the room
with the other kids

on small red chairs

they're eating oranges
and crackers with herring pâté

cardboard hearts and stars dangle from the ceiling

I squat down next to her

hi Evy

would you like to go home with me to Daddy?

she puts her cracker down

what's that on your forehead?

she points to the barbwire scar

it's nothing

she brushes my bangs to the side
and cocks her head

does it hurt?

no I say and turn my face away

she takes hold of my head and turns it

close your eyes she says

then she blows on my face

her breath is warm

it smells of herring pâté

she blows and blows

the scar prickles

then it gets warm

the heat runs up across my head

down my neck

along my spine

and spreads to my entire body

Evy lets go of my head

there she says

I open my eyes

feel with my fingers

the skin of my forehead's completely smooth

she leans in toward me
and kisses me on the mouth

the other kids clap and whoop

Evy crawls up on her chair

she raises her arms in the air

the sunlight falls through the window
and sets fire to the glasses

the orange peels glow orange

the children join hands
and start to sing

Evy tilts her head back and shuts her eyes

her feet rise

the children's voices rise

and she floats among the Christmas decorations

higher and higher

*

where've you been?

hey have you been crying?

my sister takes me by the shoulders

no no it's all right

I remove her hands

what's that for?

she's pointing at the fifth of vodka under my arm

just for the mulled wine I say
and go out in the kitchen to Thomas

*

my sister says
I smoke and drink too much

I say that it's canceled out
by my reading

if I mustn't think of you
when I think of happiness

I think of chilled vodka
sliding through me

*

Nightwatch is a success

because the students know Nikolaj Coster-Waldau
from Game of Thrones

it's contrapuntal

says Christina about the scene
where Ulf Pilgaard thrusts a knife up in Joyce
to the sounds of Little Lise Light on Her Feet

yes I say
and go out to the restroom
and google *contrapuntal*

the white sheets over the corpses
might symbolize innocence says Sandra

no I say

the white sheets are just white sheets

she gives me a long look

you can't know that

yes I say

and get an urge to place a thumb
on each of her eyelids

push her eyes in

I can

*

do you actually smoke

since you carry a lighter? Otto S asks

I'm about to light the calendar candle
that Noah just bought
even though we're in the middle of December

at parties I say

then I dismiss them

it's a half hour before the bell

I sit at my desk
in the blue light of the film projector

I close my eyes

the agitation doesn't sit in one part of my body

it migrates

*

it's below freezing

I lay sleeping when you called

now we're sitting on a bench by the Lakes

you taste of beer

you've been out with the boys

your hand's cold against my neck

my belly

my thigh

blood runs to the heart

blood runs to the cock

it hurts
the colored light in my brain

I have an urge to let it all go

to piss upon your hand

*

the thirteenth time I see you naked

you can't come

sorry

I really don't know what's going on

you say

*

I'm drinking white wine to cool my furious cunt

I don't inflict violence on anything except my own body

the heart the cunt the longings

*

the fourteenth time I see you naked

I see you only in the mirror

you turned me around at the start

you're too hard

neither of us says a thing
when we sit in the carriage afterward

*

we sit on a bench in Ringsted and smoke

your left hand rests on my thigh

you're not wearing gloves

your hands drive me crazy

the devil's dormant in my blood

do you know that?

I think I've got to
postpone it you say

just a little while

we've talked about going to Bali
over New Year's

we can get it cheap through my work

maybe it'll be good
so that I can have some calm

you know

to think it through
how exactly I'm going to

you're not looking at me

I take a deep drag

and stub out the cigarette on your hand

*

I sit in bed
with the telephone in front of me

I sit on the train
with the telephone in front of me

I sit at my desk in school
with the telephone in front of me

bed train desk

bed train desk

three days pass

ten years pass

you think of me seldom
and only feel

a slight twitch in your prick

it makes me start

but the text is from my mom:

wish list?

*

you're standing on the platform

you've got a bandage on your hand

you tremble when you kiss me

you're crazy you say

you're crazy I say

*

high school gala

and I've overdone it

it's really important
not to outshine the students says BROM

she's wearing flats and a feather boa

there are white cloths on the long tables

menus and occasional songs under the plates

seems as if everyone's decked out

the students like young newlyweds

the teachers like old confirmands

STAR and LUST dance well

I've said no
to the teachers' quadrille

everyone drinks wine with the meal

the music teachers have formed a band
and play Happy by Pharrell

the senior class votes FLIB Teacher of the Year

he struts between the tables
in a suit and Chinese slippers

it's actually a bit unfair that the same teacher
can win multiple times says STAR

when you just make films with your classes
it's a cinch to be popular says BROM

where you going? a sophomore asks

she's in a black pantsuit
with a low back

she's standing with her phone in front of the main entrance

home I say

I walk over to the parking lot

we've agreed to meet
on the platform at eleven

you've been at a Christmas party for work

you're handsome in a tie

I'm tall in stilettos

you've got beer in your bag
which we drink on the train

we get off at Ringsted

find a barroom

a corner

we kiss

we buy beer on tap

in bottles

G & T's

kiss more drink more

you balance a tray

two apiece you say

and place four Fernet-Brancas before me

we hammer the empty glasses down on the table

you laugh

you chain-smoke
with a slight tremor in your hand

I have to pee and get up

trip over the shadows of the chair legs

you try to help me up
and drop the cigarette on your arm

ouch God

dammit

you're slurring

it's burnt a hole in your shirt

you cup your hands around my face

sorry you say

I'm on my knees

my eyes swim up toward yours
like spawning fish
in an aquarium full of vodka

you're squinting

your face is slack

you're so butt-ugly I say into your mouth

you taste of liquor and smoke

your phone blinks on the table

it's Maria

you flip it over

she's standing in front of the living room window
looking down into the courtyard

it stops ringing and goes to voicemail

she scrolls through her contacts

he left quite early
somewhere around ten maybe
your coworker tells her

then Evy's standing in the doorway

Maria waves her over

she pads across the floor with her blanket

hasn't he come home?

no says Maria
and runs a hand through Evy's hair

I really don't get it

I'm sure he'll be home soon your coworker says

where's Daddy? Evy asks when they're sitting on the couch

he'll be home soon says Maria

her pulse is rapid

she taps out 112

deletes the numbers

then checks the train times again
even though she knows
the last one left a long time ago

she sends a text:

WHERE ARE YOU?!

you press your forehead against mine
so hard it hurts

I hold your head

then suddenly you tear yourself free
grab your coat
and plunge through the bar

the door closes

the bartender looks at me

I fall getting out of the taxi

skin my palm

the driver's idling his engine

he rolls down a window

can you manage?

I wave to him
and go over toward the main entrance

he rolls up the window and drives off

I fling my stilettos into a bush

hey what are you doing?

a student in a navy-blue suit is standing and pissing

shhh I tell him

techno when I step into the assembly hall

torturously loud

my nylons stick to the floor

a chaos of people

three girls dance on a table

their hairdos have fallen

someone waves over by the wall

it's EMO

the teachers sit together at a table

STAR lifts a bottle in the air when he sees me

I act as if I don't see them

walk toward the dance floor in the middle

can you turn it up louder?

Otto P's behind the mixer

louder louder! I shout in his ear

I take his beer
and slide out onto the floor

I want more bass in my chest

so my heart explodes

I want to die

I want to dance

thick smoke tumbles out of the smoke machine

I move around in it

your mouth

I weigh nothing

my heart is spinning

around and around

the students with their arms raised

they dance badly and with abandon

they kiss each other

your tongue in my ear

all sound vanishing

the light flashing

someone steps on my foot with a stiletto heel

it doesn't hurt

the sun plummets from the sky
and into your hands

I want to remember that

I want to drink my beer
but I've dropped it

you're running through my face

my heart is a disco ball

my cunt a piece of rotting meat

your semen silvery

then the students' heads topple
and roll around the floor

the bodies keep dancing

I want to touch them

but my hands are made of smoke

my body's made of smoke
that explodes in all directions

Noah stands in the center of it all
the smoke surging around him

he turns his head in slow motion

he smiles

his teeth are phosphorescent

*

I think it must be something I ate

I clear my throat

and then I had maybe
a bit too much wine with dinner

the principal looks at me

are you happy here?

she's got thick gray hair

I haven't talked to her since I started

stick or carrot

I remember she asked during the interview
and that her hair was in a thick braid

neither one I answered

with something about happy learning

she looks at me gravely

yes I say

yes I'm very happy to be here

she pushes back her chair
folds one leg over the other

of course there has been a bit of

shall we say

lurching?

she holds my gaze

I know that it's difficult at the start

it's straight to the lions

are you remembering to relax?

yes I say

because that's important she says

one needs to restitute

it'll soon be Christmas break
and then you must take care of yourself

recharge the batteries

then we'll see in January

how it goes

whether you've got things a bit more under control

*

there aren't any students
when I get up to the classroom

I walk over to the window

most of them are standing under the roof
by the parking lot and smoking

with no coats

as if they never get cold

Bilka gleams in the background

Noah stands next to the vomit girl

she wears a Santa hat

I lie in the middle of the dance floor

with my head on BROM's lap

go away! shouts STAR

Noah holds a water bottle to my mouth

that's the last thing I remember from the gala

I came to on EMO's sofa

Otto S claps Noah on the shoulder

Noah turns toward him

then they're singing something together

that's what it looks like anyhow

they move their mouths in unison

everyone laughs

Otto S pokes his head between
Noah's legs and stands up

Noah's sitting on his shoulders

he spreads his arms as if he's flying

he grabs the vomit girl's Santa hat

she takes a swing at him

then they all turn their heads
toward the entrance somewhere below me

Otto S bends down and Noah hops off

they flick away their smokes and go inside

we're all to dance around the Christmas tree in the assembly hall

no no no! yells BROM

you guys go left!

she's coordinating the dance with KILI

they want us to form three rings
that move in different directions

it takes a long time to get it to work

I'd like to see it from above

we sing Fair Is Creation

I stand between STAR and EMO

STAR gives my hand a squeeze

he sent me a text the next day

chin up
you passed out and so what?
it happens

Noah's pulled his hood forward
so I can't see his face

*

we walk around West Cemetery

it's the twenty-third of December

you've asked me if we should go for a walk

we walk and walk

it's almost a shame
we're disturbing the snow I say

you're very quiet

then you stop

it's too much
that we're going to have that conversation here

it's too dramatic

you say we're going to be adults

here's a Faroese section
and a Greenlandic section

a Muslim section

a memorial to fallen soldiers

a gravestone for British sailors

a mass grave

spruces

gravel paths

Herman Bang lies here

Emil Bønnelycke lies here

there's a pond as well

surrounded by plantings
and graves of prime ministers

by the pond there's also a bench
you can sit on in the summer

with a view of a chapel
that has yellow tiles over the entrance

they shine like gold
when the sun falls upon them

Citations

p. 91   *I walk with my lantern …*
Lyrics translated from 'Jeg går med min lanterne',
author unknown

p. 146 *thank you for the shining day that is departed*
Translated from 'Du som har tændt millioner af stjerner',
lyrics by Johannes Johansen, 1981 and 1982

p. 148 stanzas beginning *and I love your hair* and
and I love / your laughter
Translated from an untitled poem that begins 'Når alt er
mørkt og der ikke er noget lys' in *Mit Indre Pompeii [My Inner
Pompeii]*, Peter-Clement Woetmann, Kronstork, 2010

p. 149 *now we shall go with a heart so red …*
Lyrics translated from 'Nu vi skal gå med et hjerte så rødt',
author unknown

p. 159 *Kvium's symbols …*
Adapted and translated from 'Dit fjols!', René Høeg,
Horsens Klosterkirke, 2014

p. 170 *girls you walk in the night …*
Translated from three fragments in 'Ophøjet', in *Rose
Tid og Evighed: Poesi og Prosa 1919–1969*, Harald Landt
Momberg, Rhodos, 1969

Additional sources of inspiration include Villy Sørensen,
Harald Landt Momberg, Christian Dorph, Dennis Gade
Kofod, Édouard Levé, Beyoncé, Martin Glaz Serup,
Sandra Holm – and no doubt others.

Biographies

Tine Høeg (b. 1985) is a Danish writer. Her novel *New Passengers* won Bogforum's Debutantpris, the prize awarded each year for the best literary debut published in Denmark. Høeg's own adaptation of the novel has been staged at the Royal Danish Theatre. She lives in Copenhagen.

Misha Hoekstra has translated numerous Danish authors, including Hans Christian Andersen and Maren Uthaug. In 2017, he received the Danish Translation Prize, and his translation of Dorthe Nors's *Mirror, Shoulder, Signal* was shortlisted for the Man Booker International Prize.

This book has been selected to receive financial assistance from English PEN's 'PEN Translates!' programme, supported by Arts Council England. English PEN exists to promote literature and our understanding of it, to uphold writers' freedoms around the world, to campaign against the persecution and imprisonment of writers for stating their views, and to promote the friendly co-operation of writers and the free exchange of ideas.
www.englishpen.org

New Passengers is No. 2 in the series
New Scandinavian Literature

Graphic design by Ard – Chuard & Nørregaard
Typeset in Basel Grotesk by Chi-Long Trieu
Printed and bound by KOPA, Lithuania, 2020

Danish Arts
Foundation

This translation was made possible through the generous support
of the Danish Arts Foundation and a PEN/Heim Translation Fund Grant

A CIP catalogue record for this book is available from the British Library

ISBN 978 1 9999928 6 6

Lolli Editions
132 Defoe House, Barbican
London EC2Y 8ND
United Kingdom
www.lollieditions.com